About the Author and This Book

Irene Daria, Ph.D. is a developmental psychologist who specializes in teaching children how to read.

She is the founder and director of StepsTutoring, a premier tutoring service in New York City, which provides private lessons in reading, writing and math to children in preschool and grades K to 12. "At StepsTutoring, we have seen that teaching children what they need to know, in our step-by-step sequential manner, causes children to love learning, motivates them to do well, and, inevitably, results in higher grades," says Dr. Daria.

This book will enable you to teach your child how to read, using the same fun, research-based, effective methods we use in our renown private lessons.

For more information, visit www.StepsTutoring.com.

www.StepstoReading.com

Printed in the U.S.A.
ISBN 978-0-9864329-2-7

ST▨PS to...
Reading

by Irene Daria, Ph.D.

Designed by Tingting Wei

Illustrations by Tingting Wei, Eryka Sajek,and Eric Wiener

Table of Contents

What this book teaches

This is Book 3 in the "Steps to Reading" series. This book teaches digraphs. These are the sounds "ch," "sh," "th" and "wh."

      This book builds on the skills taught in Steps to Reading Book 1 and Book 2. Book 1 teaches children short vowels in three-letter words like "cat" and "hop." Book 2 teaches blends. These are longer words like "clap" and "hand" in which two consonants at the beginning and/or end of words are sounded out. If your student has not yet mastered short vowels or blends, complete Steps to Reading Book 1 and/or Book 2 before doing this book.

Supplemental materials

The books listed below are great practice for the skills your student will be learning as he or she progresses through the lessons in this book.

- "The Alphabet Series, Volume 1," compiled by Frances Bloom. This is a set of 18 little books published by Educators Publishing Service. If you have used Steps to Reading Books 1 and 2 with your student, then you probably already have this set. We will be using three of them ("Chip Had a Hut," "Tish the Fish," and "A Wish for Yak") with this workbook.

- "One Fish, Two Fish, Red Fish, Blue Fish," by Dr. Seuss.

- "Now I'm Reading! Level One: Animal Antics." This is a boxed set of early readers by Nora Gaydos published by Innovative Kids. There are several "level one" sets. Make sure you buy the one called "Animal Antics." If you have used Steps to Reading Books 1 and 2 with your student, then you probably already have this set.

'ch' says
'ch' as in chick

Instructions

Say to the child: "**When the letters c and h stand side by side, you do not sound them out. Instead, they combine to make a special sound. They say, 'ch' as in the words chick and chin.**"

Say: **"Circle the letters at the beginning of the word the picture shows."** Tell the child the pictures show: chip, chick, chin, chop, check, and chimp.

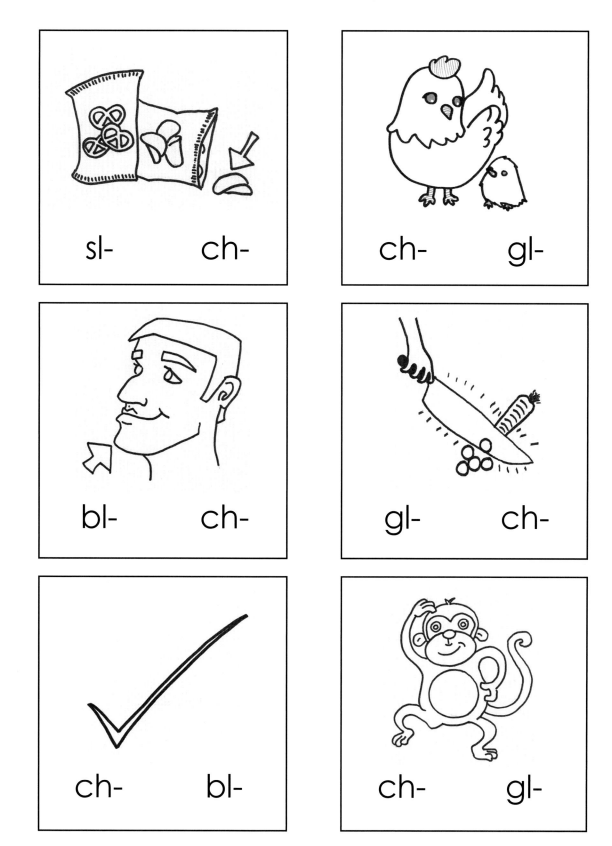

sl-   ch-

ch-   gl-

bl-   ch-

gl-   ch-

ch-   bl-

ch-   gl-

Write a word

Say: "**Write 'ch' on the blank lines and read the words out loud.**"

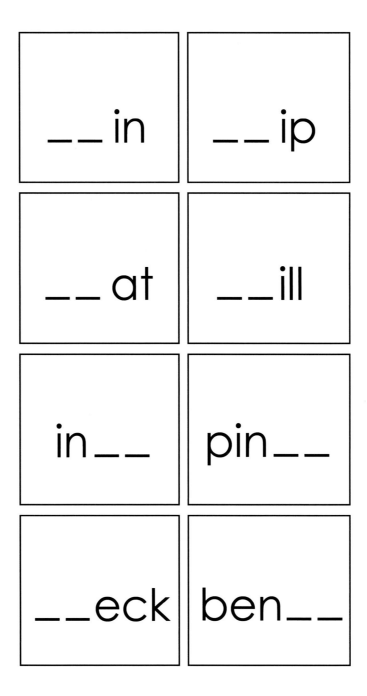

__ in	__ ip
__ at	__ ill
in __	pin __
__ eck	ben __

Say: "**Read each word out loud. Circle the word that goes with the picture.**"

chin   chop

chick   chuck

chimp   chomp

chop   chip

chill   check

bench   punch

Write the word and circle the picture

chip

— — — —

chop

— — — —

chimp

— — — — —

chin

— — — —

chick

— — — — —

bench

— — — — —

Draw a line from the word to the picture

Say: **"Read each word out loud. Then draw a line from the correct word to the picture."**

chip

chop

chap

limp

chimp

chomp

pin

chin

slim

rich

inch

pinch

peck

deck

check

bench

bunch

pinch

Vocabulary

chat

To talk.

Example: **I had a chat with my friend.**

bunch

A group of the same thing.

Example: **I ate a bunch of grapes.**

chill

To make colder.

Example: **I need to chill the lemonade.**

chuck

To throw.

Example: **Chuck the ball over here.**

chimp

An ape.

Example: **The chimp in the zoo is so cute!**

chomp

To chew loudly.

Example: **He chomped as he ate the sandwich.**

Circle the letters

Say: "**Circle the correct letters. Then write the word.**" Tell the child what each picture represents: inch, chimp, chip, bench, chin, check.

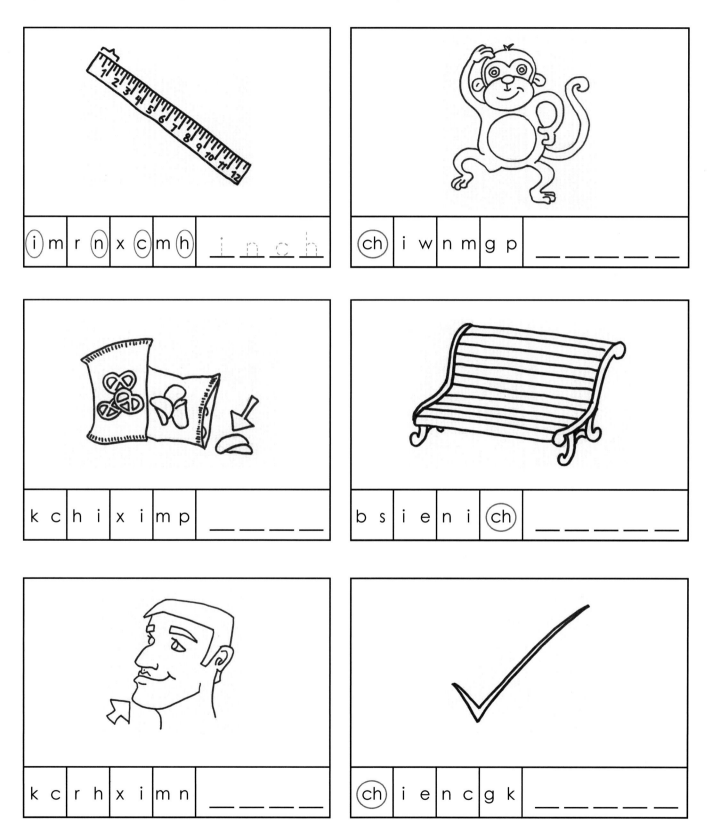

ⓘ m r ⓝ x ⓒ m ⓗ   _i_ _n_ _c_ _h_

ⓒⓗ i w n m g p   _ _ _ _ _ _

k c h i x i m p   _ _ _ _ _ _

b s i e n i ⓒⓗ   _ _ _ _ _ _

k c r h x i m n   _ _ _ _ _

ⓒⓗ i e n c g k   _ _ _ _ _ _

Play Bingo with "ch" words

Instructions

Materials: • Flashcards. Cut out the cards on the opposite page.
   • 2 gameboards follow the flashcards. In Bingo, every player gets his or her own gameboard. You and the child should each select a gameboard to use.
   • Pennies to use as game pieces.

1. Place the flashcards in one stack, with the words facing up.
2. Have the child read the word on the top card in the stack.
3. Each of you should look for that word on your Bingo boards and place a penny on top of the word on your boards when you find it.
4. Place the card the child read face down on the table.
5. Repeat steps 2-4. The child should be the one doing all of the reading of the words on the flashcards. Continue until one of you has three pennies in a row, either horizontally, vertically, or diagonally. The first player to get three in a row should call out, "Bingo!" That player wins the game.

Bingo Flashcards

Cut out the cards along the dotted lines.

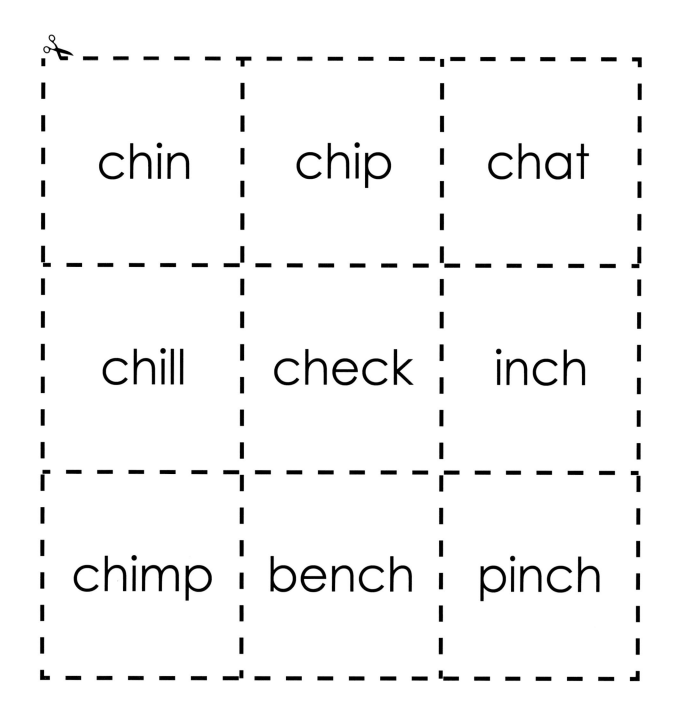

chin	chip	chat
chill	check	inch
chimp	bench	pinch

This page is intentionally left blank.

This page is intentionally left blank.

BINGO

chin	chip	chat
chill	check	inch
chimp	bench	pinch

BINGO

check	chimp	inch
chat	chin	bench
chip	pinch	chill

What you need to know about...
Sight Words

"Sight Words" are words the child needs to memorize, as opposed to sound out. Sight words either do not follow phonics rules (and, so, cannot be sounded out) or they are very common words that follow phonics rules the child has not yet learned.

The sight words in this book are presented in the order they will appear in the stories children will be reading as they make their way through this book. I call them "power words" because knowing how to read these sight words will increase the child's reading power. Since these words are so common in stories, memorizing them will enable your child to read many books much more quickly.

If your student completed the first two books in this "Steps to Reading" series, then he or she knows the 24 most common sight words. (They are listed on the following pages.) If your student did not complete Book 1 or 2, make sure your student knows these words before proceeding.

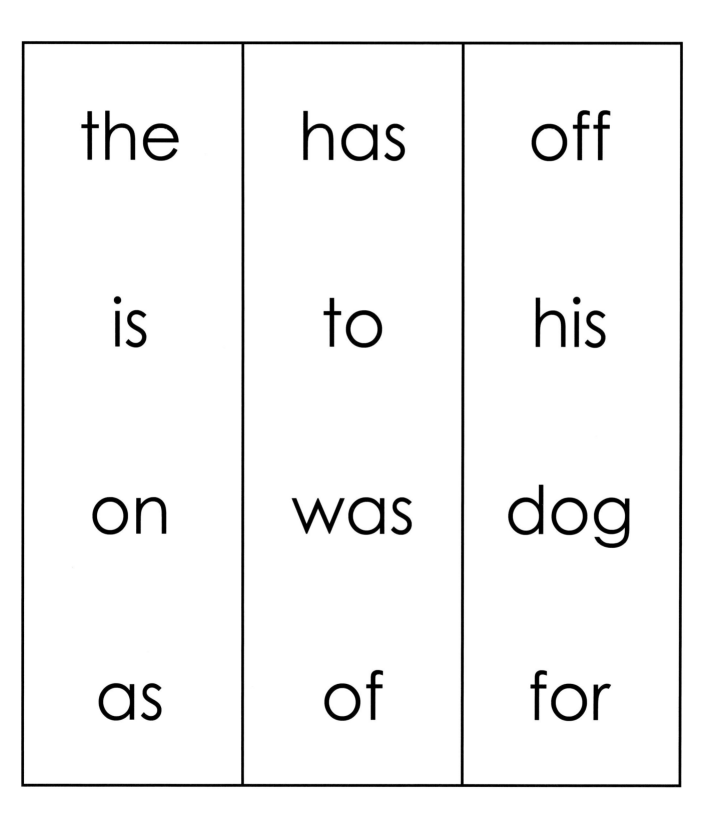

the	has	off
is	to	his
on	was	dog
as	of	for

Second set of Power Words

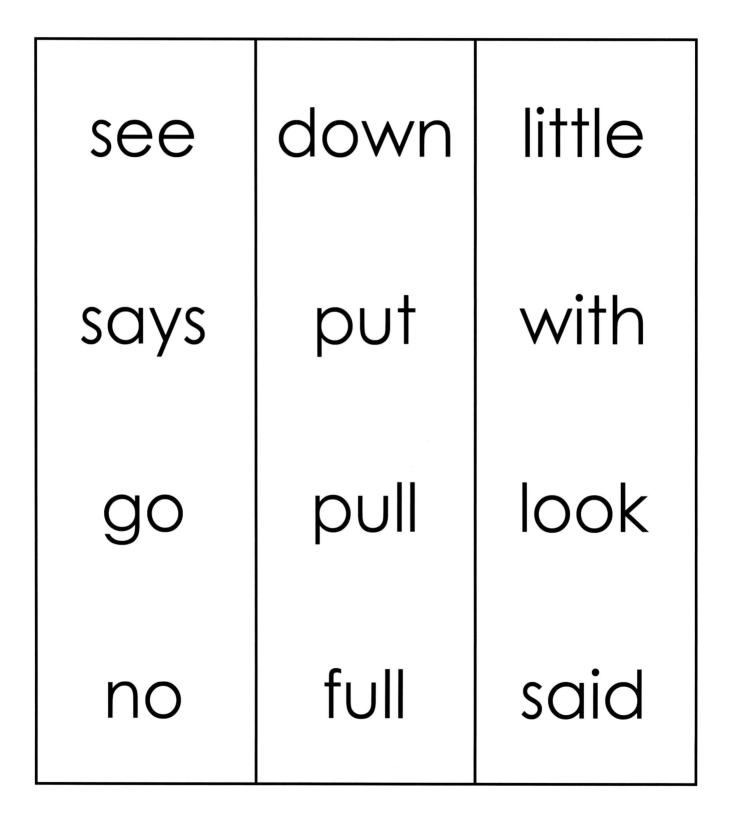

see	down	little
says	put	with
go	pull	look
no	full	said

Instructions

1. Say: "**Some words don't follow any of the sounding-out rules. They are words that just need to be memorized. We will call them 'power words' because they are words that appear very often in the stories you will be reading. Knowing these words will really boost your reading power.**
2. Point to the word "have," *above*. Say, "**This word is 'have.'**"
3. On the following page, your student will trace and write the word "have."
4. Any time you come to a Power Word lesson in this book, read the word to the child and have him or her trace and write the word on the lines that follow.

Write the Word

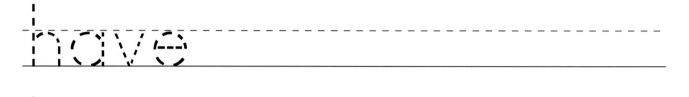

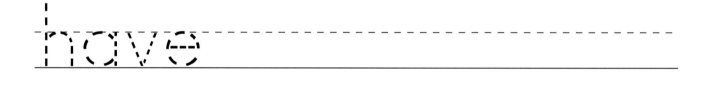

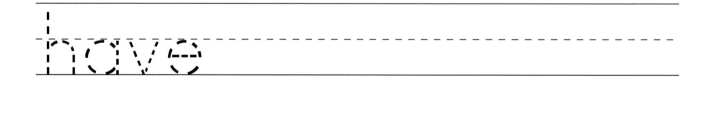

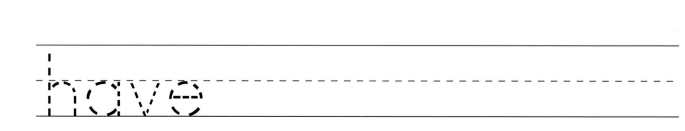

Does the sentence make sense?

Say: "**Read each sentence out loud. Color in the smiley face if the sentence makes sense, and the frown if it does not.**"

I have a rich chimp that is sick, said the fox.

I have to say cluck, said the chick.

I have to chomp on the chip, said the man.

I have to pinch his chin, said the chimp.

I have to punch the mat, said the chick.

I have to peck the stamp, said the chick.

I have a bunch of chicks that did swim, said the man.

I have to chop the block, said the duck.

Play the "ch" board game

First one to reach the end wins!

Instructions

<u>Materials you will need</u>: • A single die.
• Coins to use as markers.
• Gameboard, *opposite page*.

1. Each player places a coin on "start."
2. Take turns rolling the die.
3. Move forward the same amount of spaces as the number on the die.
4. As you move forward on the board, make the sound of the letters, or read the word, that you pass and land on.
5. For example, if a five comes up on the die, move five spaces on the game board and read five words and/or sounds.
6. The first person to reach the end wins.

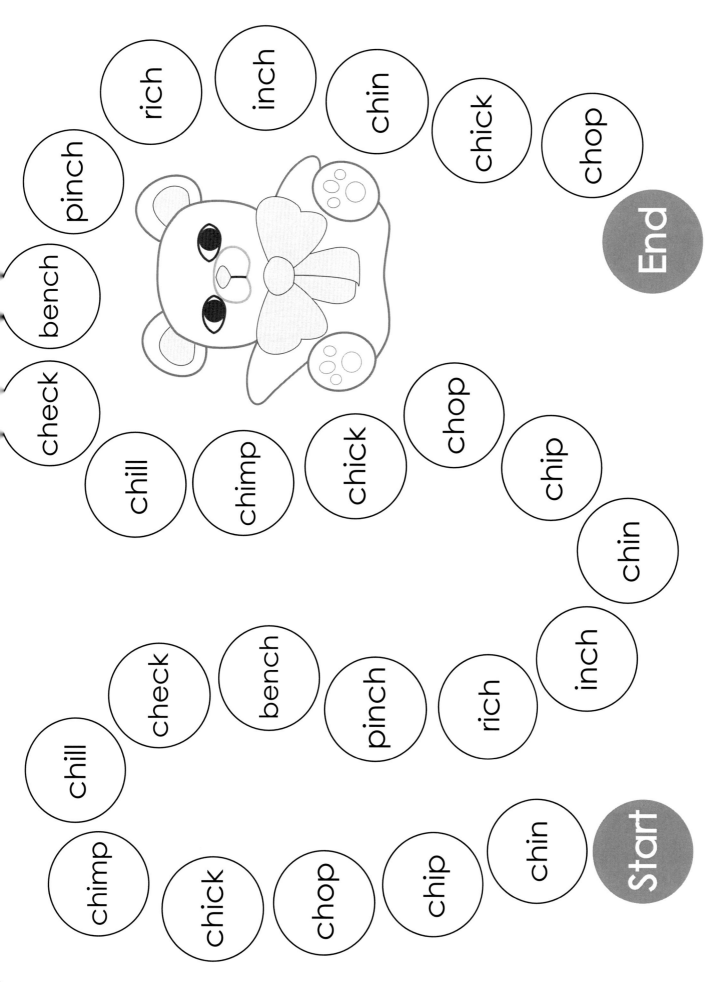

rich

inch

chin

chick

chop

pinch

End

bench

check

chill

chimp

chick

chop

chip

chin

check

bench

pinch

rich

inch

chill

chimp

chick

chop

chip

chin

Start

This is Chick.

Chick was sad.

Then Chick got a pal.

This is Hal.

All is well.

They have fun.

They run.

They kick the ball.

They jump and skip.

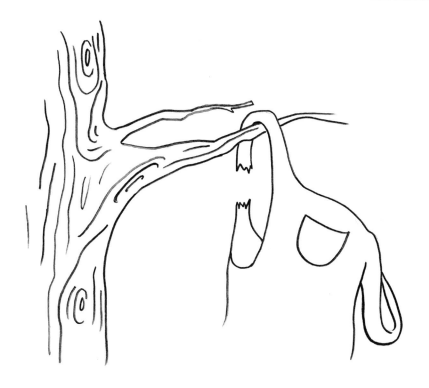

Hal's pants rip.

They went back.

And got a sack.

He put it on.

And had more fun!

Word Box

bunch
chick
chimp
pinch
chin
check
chill
bench
chop
chip

Across

1. A seat for more than two people.
4. An ape.
5. A written mark that means something is correct.
6. The bottom of your face.
7. To cut into smaller pieces.

Down

1. Three of more of something.
2. A baby chicken.
3. To squeeze between two fingers.
5. To make colder.
6. A salty snack food.

ch puzzle answers

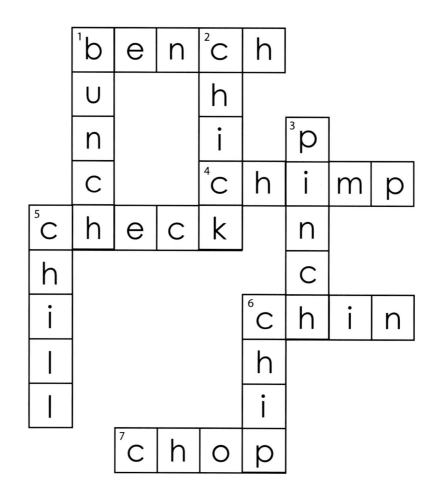

Instructions

Read a book

The child should read:

- "Chip Had a Hut," by Mary Geiger.
  This is book 7 in The Alphabet Series.
  See "Supplemental Materials, p. ii.

'sh' says
'sh' as in ship

Instructions

Say to the child: **"The letters 'sh' say 'sh' as in the words ship, shop, and shell."**

Say: "**For the top two pictures, circle the letters you hear at the beginning of the word the picture shows. The pictures show ship and shell. For the rest of the words, circle the letters you hear at the end of the word. The pictures show cash, fish, dish, and trash.**"

sh-　　ch-　　　　ch-　　sh-

-sh　　-ch　　　　-sh　　-ch

-ch　　-sh　　　　-ch　　-sh

Write a word

Say: **"Write 'sh' on the blank lines and read the words out loud."**

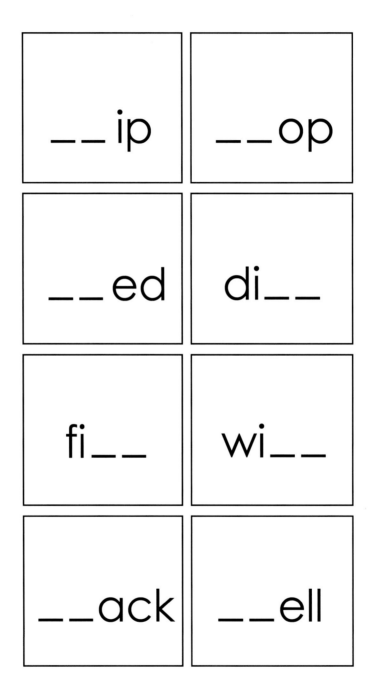

__ip   __op

__ed   di__

fi__   wi__

__ack   __ell

Which word is it?

Say: "**Read each word out loud. Circle the word that goes with the picture.**"

ship   slip

mash   cash

fish   wish

tell   shell

trash   track

wish   dish

Write the word and circle the picture

Say: "**Read the word out loud. Then write the word, and circle the picture that shows the word.**"

fish

— — — —

dish

— — — —

cash

— — — — —

ship

— — — —

trash

— — — — —

shell

— — — — —

Draw a line from the word to the picture

Say: "**Read each word out loud. Then draw a line from the correct word to the picture.**"

wish
fish
dish

shop
stop
ship

rash
cash
mash

dish
hush
wish

shed
trash
shin

shock
shell
smell

Circle the letters

Say: "**Circle the correct letters. Then write the word.**" Tell the child what each picture represents: dish, fish, ship, cash, shell, trash.

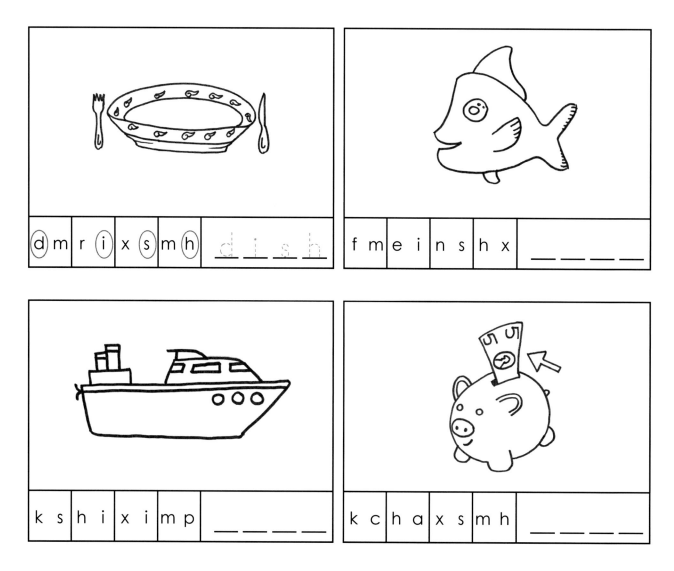

(d) m r (i) x (s) m (h)   d i s h

f m e i n s h x   _ _ _ _

k s h i x i m p   _ _ _ _

k c h a x s m h   _ _ _ _

(sh) i e n l g l   _ _ _ _ _

t k r e a c (sh)   _ _ _ _ _

Play Bingo!

This Bingo game reinforces the sounds of "sh" and "ch." Cut out the flashcards on this page and play using the two Bingo boards on the following pages. (The big X in the center of each of the gameboards that follow is a "free" space. Each of you can use that space on your boards to get five in a row.) Have fun!

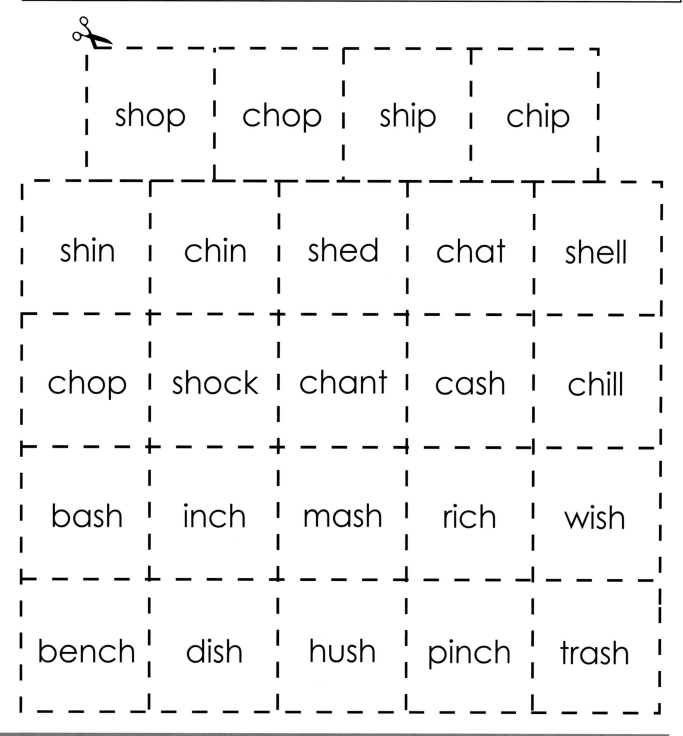

shop	chop	ship	chip	
shin	chin	shed	chat	shell
chop	shock	chant	cash	chill
bash	inch	mash	rich	wish
bench	dish	hush	pinch	trash

This page is intentionally left blank.

This page is intentionally left blank.

BINGO

shop	chop	ship	chip	chop
shin	chin	shed	chat	shell
shock	chant	✕	cash	chill
bash	inch	mash	rich	wish
bench	dish	hush	pinch	trash

BINGO

shin	chin	shell	cash	chip
chop	shop	chill	shed	bash
inch	chat	✕	chop	mash
dish	ship	chant	shock	pinch
hush	rich	bench	wish	trash

Does the sentence make sense?

Say: "**Read each sentence out loud. Color in the smiley face if the sentence makes sense, and the frown if it does not.**"

Put out the trash in the bag.	☺	☹

The fish did wish to go out.	☺	☹

Pull out the dish.	☺	☹

The duck did wish to pull out the cash.	☺	☹

The chick did pull out the shell.	☺	☹

Put out the fish in the shop.	☺	☹

Pull out the bench.	☺	☹

Pull out the cash in the bank.	☺	☹

Play the "sh" and "ch" board game!

First one to reach the end wins!

Instructions

Materials you will need: • A single die.
                                     • Coins to use as markers.
                                     • Gameboard, *opposite page*.

1. Each player places a coin on "start."
2. Take turns rolling the die.
3. Move forward the same amount of spaces as the number on the die.
4. As you move forward on the board, make the sound of the letters, or read the word, that you pass and land on.
5. For example, if a five comes up on the die, move five spaces on the game board and read five words and/or sounds.
6. The first person to reach the end wins.

Vocabulary

shed

A small building used to store things.

Example: **He kept his tools in the shed.**

shin

The front of your leg from knee to ankle.

Example: **His shin was bruised.**

stash

To store.

Example: **Stash your shoes in the closet.**

hush

Hush.

Example: **A hush fell over the crowd.**

smash

To bang hard.

Example: **He smashed his thumb with the hammer.**

shack

A small house.

Example: **He lived in a shack in the woods.**

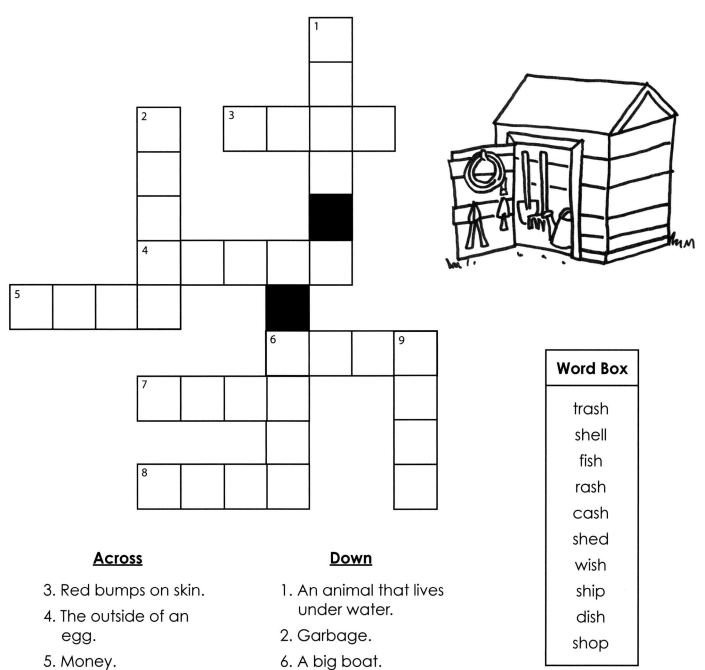

Across

3. Red bumps on skin.
4. The outside of an egg.
5. Money.
6. A small building usually used for storage.
7. To want something.
8. To buy things in a store.

Down

1. An animal that lives under water.
2. Garbage.
6. A big boat.
9. Another word for plate.

Word Box

trash
shell
fish
rash
cash
shed
wish
ship
dish
shop

sh puzzle answers

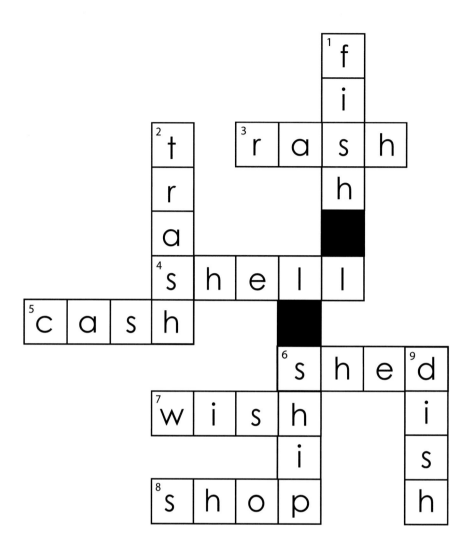

Instructions

Read a book

The child can now read:

- "Fish Gift." This is book 8 in the "Animal Antics" boxed set by Nora Gaydos.

- "Tish the Fish." This is book 14 in the Alphabet Series.
  See "Supplemental Materials," p. ii.

'th' says
'th' as in thorn

Instructions

Say to the child: **"The letters 'th' say 'th' as in the words the, that, and thorn."**

Say: "**For the top four pictures, circle the letters you hear at the end of the word the picture shows. The pictures show teeth, bath, math, and path. For the rest of the words, circle the letters you hear at the beginning of the word. The pictures show thick and think.**"

ch   th   th   sh

ch   th   th   sh

th   ch   th   sh

Write a word

Say: "**Write 'th' on the blank lines and read the words out loud.**"

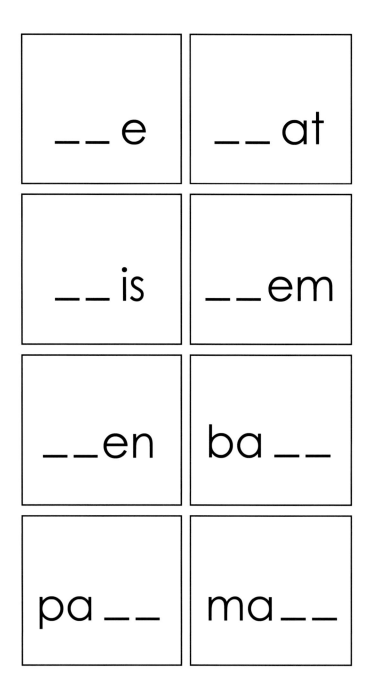

__ e   __ at

__ is   __ em

__ en   ba __

pa __   ma __

Say: "**Read each word out loud. Circle the word that goes with the picture.**"

bath   math

teeth   tuck

math   path

bath   path

thick   slick

think   ring

Write the word and circle the picture

Say: "**Read the word out loud. Then write the word, and circle the picture that shows the word.**"

path

__ __ __ __

bath

__ __ __ __

math

__ __ __ __

teeth

__ __ __ __ __

thick

__ __ __ __ __

think

__ __ __ __ __

Draw a line from the word to the picture

Say: "**Read each word out loud. Then draw a line from the correct word to the picture.**"

bath
math
path

$2+2=4$

meet
teeth
sweet

this
them
path

bath
that
math

sick
thick
slick

drink
think
thank

Play "th," "ch," and "sh" Bingo

Instructions

Materials: • Flashcards. Cut out the cards on the opposite page.
- 2 gameboards follow the flashcards. In Bingo, every player gets his or her own gameboard. You and the child should each select a gameboard to use.
- Pennies to use as game pieces.

1. Place the flashcards in one stack, with the words facing up.
2. Have the child read the word on the top card in the stack.
3. Each of you should look for that word on your Bingo boards and place a penny on top of the word on your boards when you find it.
4. Place the card the child read face down on the table.
5. Repeat steps 2-4. The child should be the one doing all of the reading of the words on the flashcards. Continue until one of you has three pennies in a row, either horizontally, vertically, or diagonally. The first player to get three in a row should call out, "Bingo!" That player wins the game.

Play Bingo!

the	bath	that	chip

this	chick	them	ship	then
shop	thin	chat	thick	chill
think	shell	thank	fish	thing
dish	path	check	math	wish

This page is intentionally left blank.

This page is intentionally left blank.

BINGO

the	bath	that	chip	this
chick	them	ship	then	shop
thin	chat	✕	thick	chill
think	shell	thank	fish	thing
dish	path	check	math	wish

BINGO

this	shell	then	dish	chip
chat	the	fish	ship	thin
them	path	✕	bath	thank
that	chick	think	shop	chill
thing	math	thick	check	wish

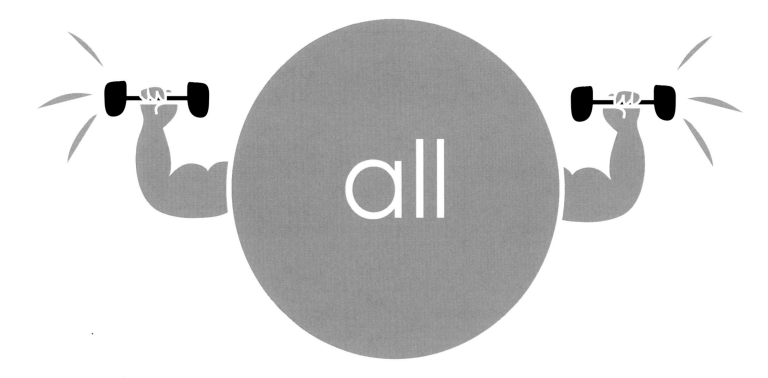

Make words that end with -all

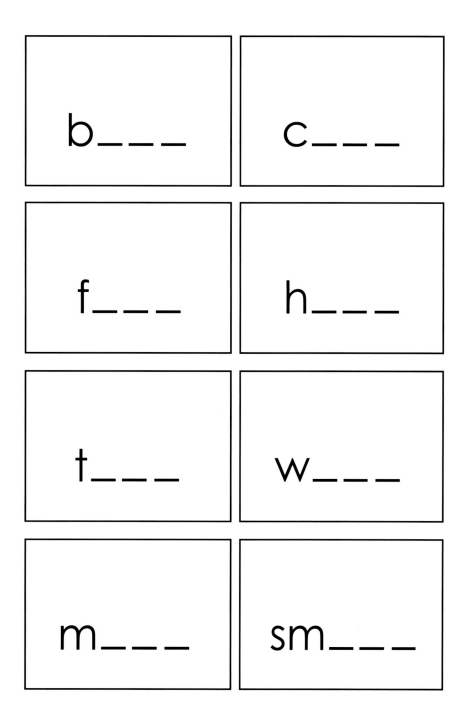

b___   c___

f___   h___

t___   w___

m___   sm___

Instructions: Have the child read out loud the words below the picture.

This is a small ball.

That is a big ball.

Instructions: Have the child read out loud the words below the picture.

This is a small wall.

That is a big wall.

Instructions: Have the child read out loud the words below the picture.

This is a small fish.

That is a big fish.

Instructions: Have the child read out loud the words below the picture.

This is a small duck.

That is a big duck.

Instructions: Have the child read out loud the words below the picture.

This is a small cat.

That is a big cat.

Word Box

teeth
thanks
thick
think
math
path
thin
bath

Across

2. You use your brain to _____.

3. A word you say when you are grateful.

6. A small road.

7. What you take in a big tub of water.

Down

1. What you chew with.

2. The opposite of thin.

4. A subject you study in school that involves numbers.

5. Another word for someone who is skinny.

th puzzle answers

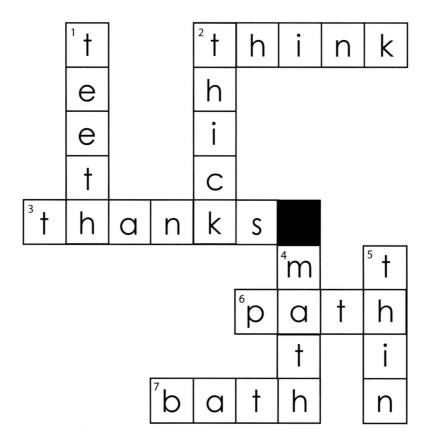

Say: "**Circle the correct letters. Then write the word.**" Tell the child what each picture represents: bath, path, math, teeth, think, thick.

Play the -th board game!

First one to reach the end wins!

Instructions

<u>Materials you will need</u>: • A single die.
• Coins to use as markers.
• Gameboard, *opposite page*.

1. Each player places a coin on "start."
2. Take turns rolling the die.
3. Move forward the same amount of spaces as the number on the die.
4. As you move forward on the board, make the sound of the letters, or read the word, that you pass and land on.
5. For example, if a five comes up on the die, move five spaces on the game board and read five words and/or sounds.
6. The first person to reach the end wins.

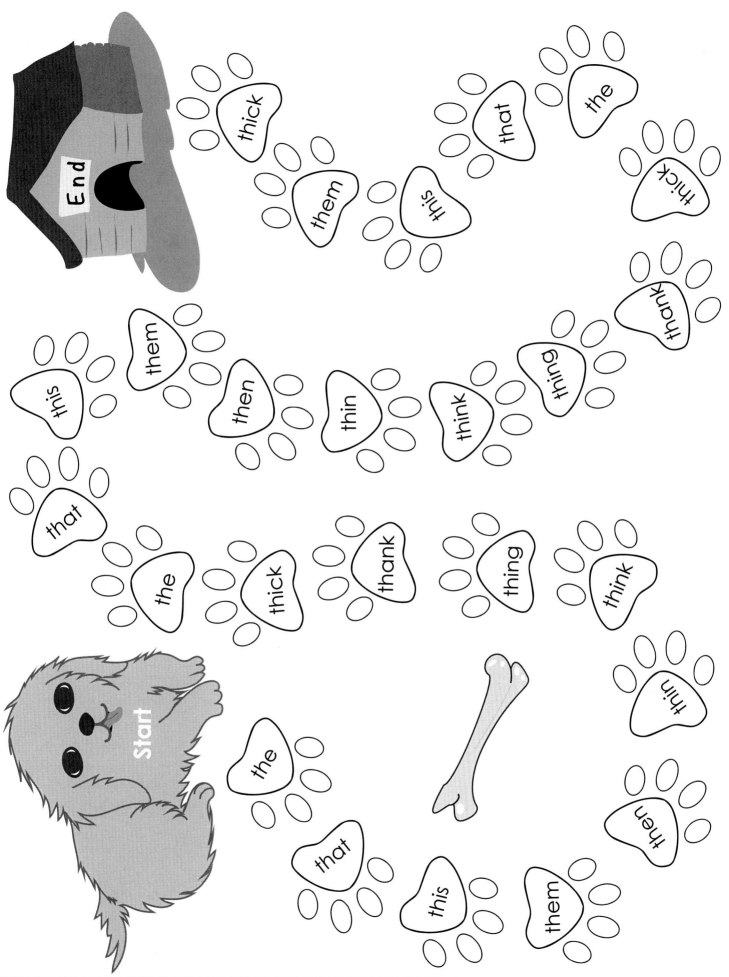

'wh' says
'w' as in whale

Instructions

Say to the child: **"The letters 'wh' say 'w' as in the words what, wheel, and whale."**

Beginning Sounds

Say: "**Write the letters that stand for the beginning sound each picture shows. The pictures show whale, chick, think, ship, thorn, whistle, chip, shed, and wheel.**"

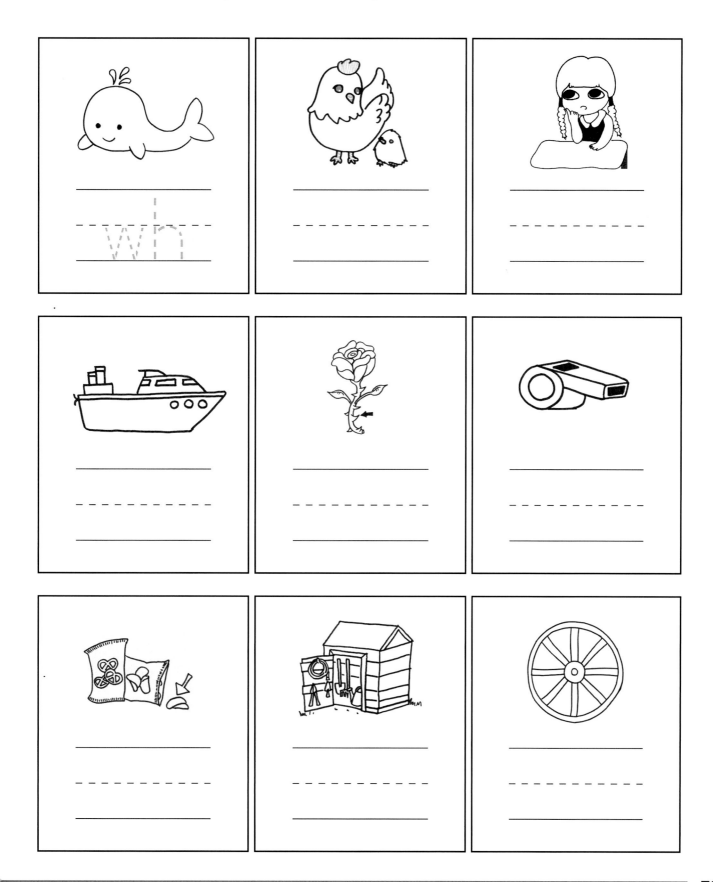

Play the wh- board game!

First one to reach the end wins!

Instructions

<u>Materials you will need</u>: • A single die.
• Coins to use as markers.
• Gameboard, *opposite page.*

1. Each player places a coin on "start."
2. Take turns rolling the die.
3. Move forward the same amount of spaces as the number on the die.
4. As you move forward on the board, make the sound of the letters, or read the word, that you pass and land on.
5. For example, if a five comes up on the die, move five spaces on the game board and read five words and/or sounds.
6. The first person to reach the end wins.

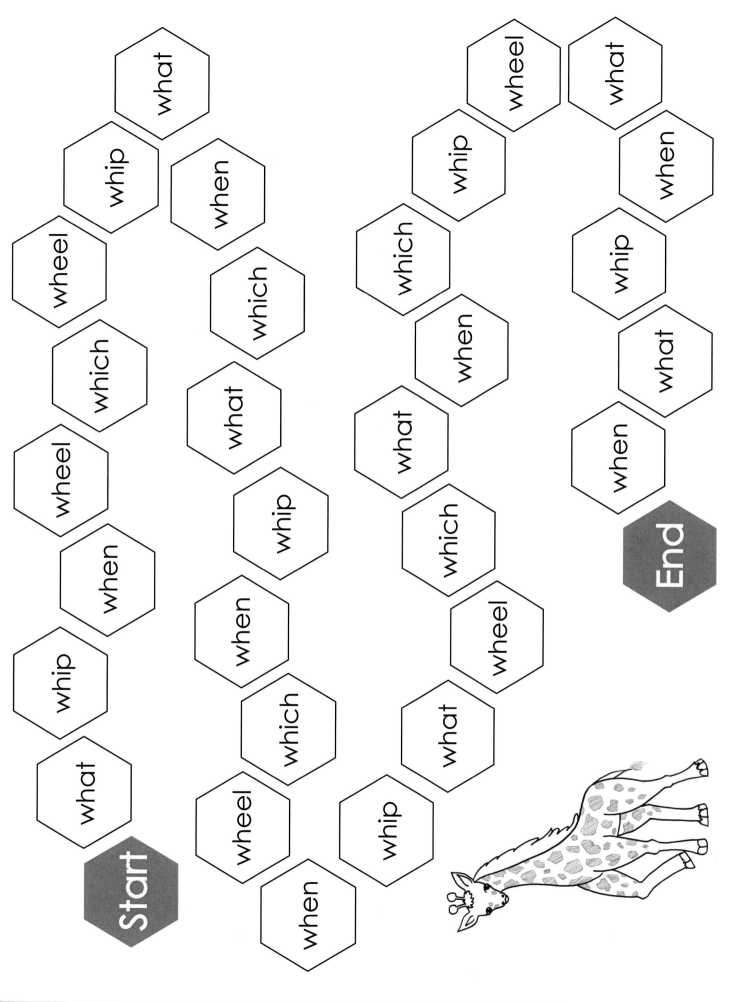

© STEPS Publishing, Inc.

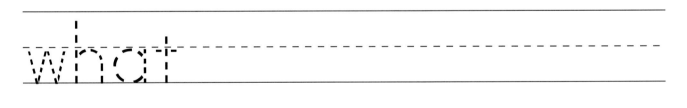

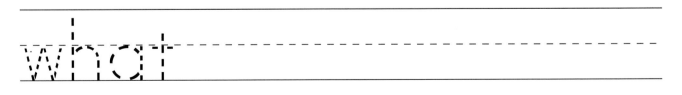

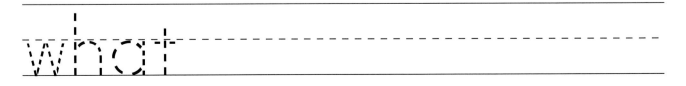

Instructions: Have the child read out loud the words below the picture.

What is that?
That is a chimp on a ship.

What is that?

What is that?
That is a dish on a bench.

Instructions: Have the child read out loud the words below the picture.

What is that?
That is a duck on the trash.

What is that?

Instructions: Have the child read out loud the words below the picture.

What is that?
That is a fish on a dish.

Instructions: Have the child read out loud the words below the picture.

What is that?
That is a chimp on a bench.

Play Review Bingo

Instructions

Materials: • Flashcards. Cut out the cards on the opposite page.
• 2 gameboards follow the flashcards. In Bingo, every player gets his or her own gameboard. You and the child should each select a gameboard to use.
• Pennies to use as game pieces.

1. Place the flashcards in one stack, with the words facing up.
2. Have the child read the word on the top card in the stack.
3. Each of you should look for that word on your Bingo boards and place a penny on top of the word on your boards when you find it.
4. Place the card the child read face down on the table.
5. Repeat steps 2-4. The child should be the one doing all of the reading of the words on the flashcards. Continue until one of you has three pennies in a row, either horizontally, vertically, or diagonally. The first player to get three in a row should call out, "Bingo!" That player wins the game.

Play Bingo!

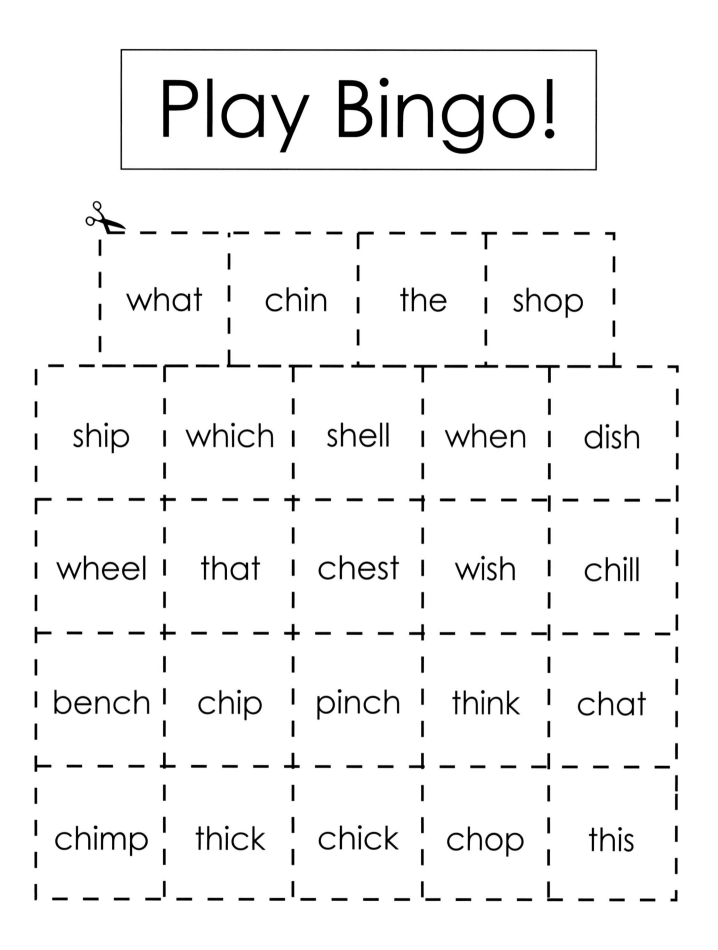

what	chin	the	shop

ship	which	shell	when	dish
wheel	that	chest	wish	chill
bench	chip	pinch	think	chat
chimp	thick	chick	chop	this

This page is intentionally left blank.

This page is intentionally left blank.

BINGO

shop	chill	dish	bench	which
think	what	the	ship	wheel
shell	chat	✕	chest	wish
chick	when	chop	chin	thick
chip	this	pinch	that	chimp

BINGO

what	chin	the	shop	ship
which	shell	when	dish	wheel
that	chest	✕	wish	chill
bench	chip	pinch	think	chat
chimp	thick	chick	chop	this

Read a book!

Instructions

Read a book

The child can now read:

- "A Wish for Yak." This is book 15 in the Alphabet Series. See "Supplemental Materials," p. ii.

Congratulations!
You've completed Step 3 in reading!

Certificate of Accomplishment

Presented to _____

Signed: _____

Date: _____